LOW-BEGINNING

Health Stories

WORKBOOK

Readings and Language Activities
for Healthy Choices

Ann Gianola
Instructor, San Diego Community College District
Instructor, University of San Diego English Language Academy
San Diego, California

New Readers Press

Health Stories: Readings and Language Activities for Healthy Choices
Low-Beginning Workbook
ISBN 978-1-56420-704-3

Copyright © 2007 New Readers Press
New Readers Press
A Publishing Division of ProLiteracy
1320 Jamesville Avenue, Syracuse, New York 13210
www.newreaderspress.com

Printed in the United States of America
9 8 7 6 5 4 3

All proceeds from the sale of New Readers Press materials
support literacy programs in the United States and worldwide.

Developmental Editor: Paula L. Schlusberg
Creative Director: Andrea Woodbury
Illustrations: George Hamblin, Seitu Hayden and Roger Audette, Represented by Wilkinson Studios Inc.
Production Specialist: Maryellen Casey

Contents

LESSON 1: Choosing Juice

Complete the story.

finds	reads	picks up	points
looks	puts down	has	drinks

Lela is at the supermarket with her mother. Her mother _____ the juices on aisle 4. Lela _____ to a big orange bottle. Lela says she _____ it at her friend's house. Her mother _____ the bottle. Then she _____ at the Nutrition Facts label. This orange juice _____ only 10% orange juice. Zahra _____ the bottle. "Sorry," she says. "I'm not buying that one. Lela's mother picks up another bottle. She _____ the label. It has 100% orange juice. She puts it in her shopping cart.

Write each sentence in the negative.

Negative

1. I drink it at my friend's house. _I don't drink it at my friend's house._

2. She finds the juices on aisle 4. _____

3. We put it in the shopping cart. _____

4. You want your family to drink it. _____

5. It has 100% orange juice. _____

Listening

Write the correct number next to each picture.

a. _____

b. _____

c. _____

d. _____

Write the percentages you hear.

1. _____

2. _____

3. _____

4. _____

5. _____

6. _____

7. _____

8. _____

9. _____

10. _____

Pronunciation and Writing

Say the words. Write the number of syllables next to each word. Underline the stressed syllable in the two- and three-syllable words. The first one is done for you.

1. <u>straw</u>berry __3__

2. juice ____

3. color ____

4. healthy ____

5. nutrition ____

6. chemicals ____

7. dye ____

8. house ____

9. sugar ____

10. aisle ____

11. delicious ____

12. bottle ____

Answer the questions.

Check the correct answer.

1. Where does Zahra look for orange juice?

____ a. at her friend's house

____ b. at the supermarket

____ c. on aisle 14

2. What is not in the big orange bottle?

____ a. water and sugar

____ b. chemicals and dye

____ c. 100% orange juice

3. How much orange juice does it have?

____ a. 100%

____ b. 10%

____ c. 50%

4. Why is Zahra not buying it?

____ a. It isn't pink.

____ b. It isn't healthy.

____ c. It isn't big.

LESSON 2: Allergic to Shellfish

Complete the sentences.

stomach	seafood	shellfish	difficult	allergic

1. Mali is at a _____ restaurant.

2. She can't eat _____.

3. Mali is _____ to it.

4. Breathing is _____ when she eats shellfish.

5. She gets a rash and an upset _____.

Rewrite the sentence.

Rewrite the sentence with different subjects. Then write negative sentences.

	Negative
1. She is allergic to shellfish.	<u>She is not allergic to shellfish.</u>
2. I _____	_____
3. You _____	_____
4. He _____	_____
5. They _____	_____

Listening

Listen to the dialog between Mali and the waiter. Put a check next to what Mali says.

1. ____ a. I'd like to order the grilled scallops.

   ____ b. I'd like to order the grilled halibut.

2. ____ a. You need to know that I am allergic to shellfish.

   ____ b. You need to know that I am not allergic to shellfish.

3. ____ a. I have a message for the waiter.

   ____ b. I have a message for the cook.

4. ____ a. Please tell him to be careful with my shellfish.

   ____ b. Please tell him to be careful with my dinner.

5. ____ a. My food can touch shellfish.

   ____ b. My food cannot touch shellfish.

6. ____ a. Ask him to clean the counter, grill, and utensils very well.

   ____ b. Ask him to clear off the counter, grill, and utensils very well.

7. ____ a. Thanks. I won't get very sick from eating a tiny amount.

   ____ b. Thanks. I can get very sick from eating a tiny amount.

Pronunciation and Writing

Say the words. Write the number of syllables next to each word. Underline the stressed syllable in the two- and three-syllable words. The first one is done for you.

1. <u>shell</u>fish _2_

2. grilled ____

3. utensils ____

4. counter ____

5. allergic ____

6. breathing ____

7. eat ____

8. crab ____

9. difficult ____

10. seafood ____

11. food ____

12. understand ____

Answer the questions.

Check the correct answer.

1. What is Mali allergic to?

   ____ a. seafood

   ____ b. shellfish

   ____ c. peanuts

2. What is difficult when she eats shellfish?

   ____ a. ordering

   ____ b. eating

   ____ c. breathing

3. What does she need if she eats shellfish?

   ____ a. medical help

   ____ b. the cook

   ____ c. the waiter

4. What does Mali want the cook to clean?

   ____ a. her dinner

   ____ b. the counter, grill, and utensils

   ____ c. the crab, lobster, and oysters

LESSON 3: Under Stress

Complete the story.

stress	hurts	doctor	teeth
work	headaches	family	relax

Salman's wife worries about her husband. He gets _____.
His neck _____. He grinds his _____. He
doesn't sleep well. Salman's wife tells him to visit the _____
on his day off. The doctor tells Salman he is under _____.
It isn't good for him. He needs to _____ more. "Don't
_____ so hard," says the doctor. "See a movie." Salman
and his _____ go to a movie. It's expensive, but everyone
has fun.

Rewrite the sentence.

Rewrite the sentence with different subjects. Then write negative sentences.

Negative

1. You are under stress. You are not under stress.

2. He _____ _____

3. They _____ _____

4. I _____ _____

5. We _____ _____

Listening

Write the correct number next to each picture.

a. ____

c. ____

b. ____

d. ____

Write the dollar amounts you hear.

1. _____

2. _____

3. _____

4. _____

5. _____

6. _____

7. _____

8. _____

9. _____

10. _____

Pronunciation and Writing

Complete each word with *er, or,* or *ur.* Then practice saying the words.

1. supp __ __ ts

2. ret __ __ ns

3. und __ __

4. theat __ __

5. doct __ __

6. w __ __ ks

7. cl __ __ k

8. manag __ __

9. ho __ __ s

10. ev __ __ yone

11. h __ __ ts

12. w __ __ ries

13. resta __ __ ant

14. popc __ __ n

15. press __ __ e

Answer the questions.

Check the correct answer.

1. What is Salman's job?

____ a. doctor

____ b. restaurant manager

____ c. clerk

2. What does he worry about?

____ a. symptoms

____ b. tests

____ c. money

3. What does the doctor say?

____ a. "That's $45."

____ b. "You are under stress."

____ c. "Let's see a movie
       tonight."

4. What does Salman need to do?

____ a. relax more

____ b. rub his neck

____ c. grind his teeth

LESSON 4: A Heavy Box

Complete the story.

squats	works	takes	holds
puts	bends	shows	tells

Nick _____ in a large warehouse. He is a supervisor.
Right now there is a heavy box on the floor. Adam needs to move it.
He _____ over to pick it up. His legs are straight. "No,"
says Nick. "You can hurt your back." Nick _____ Adam
how to lift a light box. He _____ down and bends at his
hips and knees only. He _____ the box close to his body.
He _____ small steps. Then he squats down again and
_____ the box down. Nick _____ Adam to
always ask for help when something is too heavy.

Rewrite the sentence.

Rewrite the sentence with different subjects. Then write negative sentences.

Negative

1. He needs to move it.   <u>He doesn't need to move it.</u>

2. They _____   _____

3. You _____   _____

4. She _____   _____

5. I _____   _____

Listening

Write the correct number next to each picture.

a. _____

c. _____

e. _____

b. _____

d. _____

What do they mean?

Listen to each sentence. Then circle what the person means.

1. a. It's too light.   b. It's too heavy.

2. a. Your legs are straight.   b. You are bending at your hips and knees.

3. a. I need help.   b. I can lift it.

4. a. Thanks for lifting it.   b. Thanks for explaining how to lift it.

5. a. You can lift the box.   b. You and I can lift the box.

Pronunciation and Writing

Complete each word from the story with two missing vowels: *a, e, i, o,* or *u.* Then practice saying the words.

1. str __ __ ght

2. w __ reho __ se

3. kn __ __ s

4. b __ x __ s

5. h __ __ vy

6. sq __ __ t

7. s __ meth __ ng

8. appr __ c __ ate

9. l __ rg __

10. cl __ s __

11. w __ lc __ me

12. s __ pervis __ r

13. m __ v __

14. ag __ __ n

15. g __ v __

Answer the questions.

Check the correct answer.

1. Where is there a heavy box?

____ a. on the steps

____ b. on the floor

____ c. on a light box

2. How are Adam's legs?

____ a. straight

____ b. heavy

____ c. hurt

3. What can Adam hurt?

____ a. his hips

____ b. his knees

____ c. his back

4. What does Adam need to do?

____ a. look for his supervisor

____ b. ask for help

____ c. pick up a light box

LESSON 5: A Shoulder Injury

Complete the sentences.

wants	helps	slips	has	falls

1. It is winter, and Julia _____ on some ice.

2. She _____ on her shoulder.

3. Julia _____ shoulder surgery.

4. Her doctor _____ her to go to physical therapy.

5. The therapist _____ Julia with her exercises.

Rewrite the sentence.

Rewrite the sentences with different subjects. Then write negative sentences.

Negative

1. Julia has a shoulder injury.   _Julia doesn't have a shoulder injury._

2. I _____   _____

3. You _____   _____

4. He _____   _____

5. She _____   _____

Listening

Listen to the dialog between Julia and her doctor. Put a check next to what the doctor says.

1. ____ a. How is your surgery feeling?

    ____ b. How is your shoulder feeling?

2. ____ a. It looks good. You can stop going to physical therapy now.

    ____ b. It looks good. You can start going to physical therapy now.

3. ____ a. Just continue your exercises at home.

    ____ b. Just continue to get stronger at home.

4. ____ a. It's fine. You can't sweep and vacuum again.

    ____ b. It's fine. You can sweep and vacuum again.

5. ____ a. But be careful on the steps. You don't want another therapy.

    ____ b. But be careful on the steps. You don't want another surgery.

6. ____ a. Do you have any other questions?

    ____ b. Do you have any other directions?

7. ____ a. You can start right away. Stretching is great exercise.

    ____ b. You can start right away. Swimming is great exercise.

Pronunciation and Writing

Say the words. Write the number of syllables next to each word. Underline the stressed syllable in the two- and three-syllable words. The first one is done for you.

1. <u>pul</u>leys __2__

2. steps ____

3. surgery ____

4. directions ____

5. vacuum ____

6. therapy ____

7. years ____

8. sweep ____

9. weights ____

10. physical ____

11. shoulder ____

12. swimming ____

Answer the questions.

Check the correct answer.

1. What does Julia need to rest?

____ a. her therapy

____ b. her coffee cup

____ c. her shoulder

2. What does the therapist help her with?

____ a. sweeping and vacuuming

____ b. rehabilitation exercises

____ c. walking down her front steps

3. When does Julia's doctor say she is OK?

____ a. after four months

____ b. three times a week

____ c. in six weeks

4. Where does Julia need to be careful?

____ a. at the swimming pool

____ b. at physical therapy

____ c. on the steps

LESSON 6: Flossing Helps

Complete the sentences.

visits	cleans	has	helps	takes

1. Eric _____ his dentist regularly.

2. Right now he _____ a lot of plaque.

3. The dentist says that flossing _____ remove plaque.

4. She gently _____ between all of Eric's teeth.

5. Eric _____ the dental floss with him.

Write each sentence in the negative.

                                                Negative

1. He takes very good care of his   _He doesn't take very good care_
   teeth.   _of his teeth._

2. I have a healthy diet.   _____

3. They use a fluoride toothpaste.   _____

4. We visit the dentist regularly.   _____

5. She has a lot of plaque.   _____

Listening

Write the correct number next to each picture.

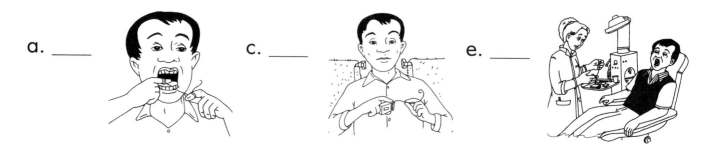

a. ____

c. ____

e. ____

b. ____

d. ____

What do they mean?

Listen to each sentence. Then circle what the person means.

1.a. Do you brush your teeth?   b. Do you clean between your teeth?

2.a. I drink them.   b. I don't drink them.

3.a. You need to brush and floss.   b. You need to brush more.

4.a. You want good teeth.   b. You want tooth decay.

5.a. I'll come again in one year.   b. I'll come again in half a year.

Pronunciation and Writing

Complete each word from the story with two missing vowels: *a, e, i, o,* or *u.* Then practice saying the words.

1. av __ __ d

2. plaq __ __

3. t __ __ thbrush

4. expl __ __ n

5. h __ __ lthy

6. dis __ __ se

7. cl __ __ ns

8. g __ __ d

9. b __ __ utiful

10. t __ __ th

11. fl __ __ ride

12. betw __ __ n

13. examinat __ __ n

14. t __ __ thpaste

15. c __ __ se

Answer the questions.

Check the correct answer.

1. What does Eric have?

____ a. tooth decay

____ b. a new toothbrush

____ c. a lot of plaque

2. What can plaque cause?

____ a. gum disease

____ b. a healthy diet

____ c. a beautiful smile

3. What can clean between Eric's teeth?

____ a. fluoride toothpaste

____ b. sodas and sweets

____ c. dental floss

4. How often does Eric need to floss?

____ a. every week

____ b. every day

____ c. in six months

LESSON 7: Two Cutting Boards

Complete the story.

hands	cutting board	meat	vegetables
soup	bacteria	food	

Alina and her mother are making _____. Alina cuts the chicken on a plastic _____. Her mother reminds Alina to wash her _____. Then Alina picks up the vegetables. She almost puts the _____ down on the same cutting board. Her mother tells her not to use the same cutting board for _____ and vegetables. She says chicken can have _____. They need to keep raw meat away from other _____. Alina uses a different cutting board.

Rewrite the sentence.

Rewrite the sentence with different subjects. Then write negative sentences.

                                               Negative

1. They are making soup.   <u>They aren't making soup.</u>

2. I _____   _____

3. We _____   _____

4. She _____   _____

5. You _____   _____

Listening

Write the correct number next to each picture.

a. _____

c. _____

e. _____

b. _____

d. _____

What do they mean?

Listen to each sentence. Then circle what the person means.

1. a. Use cold water.
   b. Use warm, soapy water.

2. a. We can get sick from bacteria.
   b. We can't get sick from bacteria.

3. a. Use the same cutting board.
   b. Use a different cutting board.

4. a. Use a lot of bleach and a little water.
   b. Use a lot of water and a little bleach.

5. a. The towel is clean.
   b. The towel is dirty.

Pronunciation and Writing

Complete each word from the story with two missing vowels: *a, e, i, o,* or *u.* Then practice saying the words.

1. l __ __ ndry

2. dr __ __ s

3. q __ __ rt

4. m __ __ t

5. s __ __ p

6. f __ __ d

7. b __ __ rd

8. c __ __ nter

9. t __ __ spoon

10. bacter __ __

11. ag __ __ n

12. bl __ __ ch

13. p __ __ ces

14. s __ __ py

15. d __ __ ghter

Answer the questions.

Check the correct answer.

1. What can chicken have?

____ a. vegetables

____ b. soapy water

____ c. bacteria

2. Where does raw meat need to be?

____ a. next to other food

____ b. away from other food

____ c. in the laundry

3. What does Svetlana hand Alina?

____ a. a different cutting board

____ b. the same cutting board

____ c. one teaspoon of chlorine bleach

4. What does Svetlana wash everything with?

____ a. warm, soapy water

____ b. hot, soapy water

____ c. 1 quart of water

LESSON 8: Getting a Refill

Complete the sentences.

| doctor | medication | refills | cabinet | pharmacy |

1. Ted takes asthma _____ every day.

2. On Thursday, Ted opens his medicine _____.

3. He has no more medication. Ted calls the _____.

4. The assistant tells Ted he has no more _____.

5. Ted needs to call his _____ right away.

Write each sentence in the negative.

	Negative
1. I have asthma.	*I don't have asthma.*
2. She takes medication every day.	_____
3. He needs a refill.	_____
4. You need to call your doctor.	_____
5. The doctor's office closes at 5:00.	_____

Days of the Week

Write the days of the week. Start with the day that comes after Sunday.

1. Sunday

2. _____   5. _____

3. _____   6. _____

4. _____   7. _____

What day does Ted call the pharmacy? _____

Listening

Circle the telephone number you hear.

1. 555-1489   555-1849

2. 555-9026   555-0926

3. 555-8137   555-8317

4. 555-2058   555-2056

5. 555-3801   555-3180

Write the number of refills you hear.

1. _____   4. _____

2. _____   5. _____

3. _____   6. _____

Pronunciation and Writing

Say the words. Write the number of syllables next to each word. Underline the stressed syllable in the two- and three-syllable words. The first one is done for you.

1. as<u>sis</u>tant _3_

2. breathe ____

3. doctor ____

4. refills ____

5. asthma ____

6. every ____

7. speaks ____

8. fax ____

9. prescription ____

10. telephone ____

11. Saturday ____

12. wait ____

Answer the questions.

Check the correct answer.

1. When does Ted take asthma medication?

   ____ a. on Saturday

   ____ b. every day

   ____ c. sometimes

2. What is it hard for Ted to do?

   ____ a. speak to the assistant

   ____ b. open his medicine cabinet

   ____ c. breathe

3. When does Ted call the pharmacy?

   ____ a. on Thursday

   ____ b. on Monday

   ____ c. on Wednesday

4. When does Ted need his medication?

   ____ a. next week

   ____ b. right away

   ____ c. on Friday

LESSON 9: Calling Poison Control

Complete the story.

bottle	mother	cap	Poison
telephone	characters	room	vitamins

This morning Connor's mother is giving him a Dancing Dog vitamin. Connor likes the _____ . They look like cartoon
_____ . Then the _____ rings. His mother forgets
to put on the child-resistant _____ . Connor picks up the
open _____ and runs. He goes to his _____ and
chews many vitamins. Now the vitamin bottle is almost empty. Connor's
_____ finds him. She runs to the telephone to call the
_____ Control center.

Rewrite the sentence.

Rewrite the sentence with different subjects. Then write negative sentences.

Negative

1. She puts the vitamins on the top shelf. — *She doesn't put the vitamins on the top shelf.*

2. We _____ _____

3. You _____ _____

4. I _____ _____

5. He _____ _____

Listening

Listen to the dialog between Kate and the operator. Put a check next to what Kate says.

1. ____ a. My son just ate one vitamin.

   ____ b. My son just ate a lot of vitamins!

2. ____ a. No, but he only ate them about 5 minutes ago.

   ____ b. No, but he only ate them about 15 minutes ago.

3. ____ a. He's five years old.

   ____ b. He's four years old.

4. ____ a. He weighs 42 pounds.

   ____ b. He weighs 44 pounds.

5. ____ a. The Dancing Dog vitamins.

   ____ b. The Dizzy Dog vitamins.

6. ____ a. I'm not sure. I think about 12.

   ____ b. I'm not sure. I think about 20.

7. ____ a. I am Kate Browning, his grandmother.

   ____ b. I am Kate Browning, his mother.

Pronunciation and Writing

Say the words. Write the number of syllables next to each word. Underline the stressed syllable in the two- and three-syllable words. The first one is done for you.

1. taste   _1_   5. upset ____   9. characters ____

2. empty   ____   6. years ____   10. shelf   ____

3. tomorrow ____   7. vitamins ____   11. poison   ____

4. telephone ____   8. children ____   12. one   ____

Answer the questions.

Check the correct answer.

1. What does Kate tell Connor?

____ a. "These taste good."

____ b. "Only one a day."

____ c. "Yum."

2. What is it dangerous for children to do?

____ a. take too many vitamins

____ b. answer the telephone

____ c. like cartoon characters

3. What does Kate forget to put on?

____ a. the answering machine

____ b. the Dancing Dog cartoon

____ c. the child resistant cap

4. What does Kate call?

____ a. the doctor's office

____ b. an ambulance

____ c. the Poison Control Center

LESSON 10: Packing for the Hospital

Complete the sentences.

drugs	hospital	list	insurance	suitcase

1. Greta is packing a _____ for her father.

2. He is going to the _____ today.

3. She puts his health _____ information inside her purse.

4. Greta gets all his prescription _____.

5. She makes a _____ of her father's allergies.

Rewrite the sentence.

Rewrite the sentence with different subjects. Then write negative sentences.

	Negative
1. He has health insurance.	_He doesn't have health insurance._
2. You _____	_____
3. We _____	_____
4. I _____	_____
5. She _____	_____

Listening

Write the correct number next to each picture.

a. _____

c. _____

e. _____

b. _____

d. _____

What do they mean?

Listen to each sentence. Then circle what the person means.

1. a. He needs to be there two or three days.

   b. He needs to be there two or three weeks.

2. a. They are in a plastic bag.

   b. They are in the bottles from the pharmacy.

3. a. He can take them.

   b. He can't take them.

4. a. You have everything you need.

   b. You don't have everything you need.

5. a. I want a magazine.

   b. I want some food.

Pronunciation and Writing

Complete each word with *er*, *or*, or *ur*. Then practice saying the words.

1. ins __ __ ance

2. raz __ __

3. all __ __ gic

4. fath __ __

5. n __ __ ses

6. rec __ __ d

7. p __ __ sonal

8. oth __ __

9. doct __ __ s

10. slipp __ __ s

11. strawb __ __ ries

12. p __ __ se

13. __ __ ganization

14. all __ __ gies

15. imp __ __ tant

Answer the questions.

Check the correct answer.

1. What does Greta put in her purse?

____ a. slippers

____ b. toothpaste

____ c. health insurance information

2. What are in their original containers?

____ a. prescription drugs

____ b. slippers

____ c. antibiotics

3. What is Greta's father allergic to?

____ a. soap

____ b. his prescription drugs

____ c. two antibiotics and strawberries

4. What does Greta's father want?

____ a. his pajamas

____ b. something to read

____ c. his razor

LESSON 11: Talking about Alcohol

Complete the story.

feels	talks	trusts	gives
promises	affects	tells	causes

Chang's father _____ about alcohol a lot. He
_____ Chang that drinking is dangerous. Alcohol
_____ a person's vision and hearing. It _____
accidents. Chang _____ never to drink and drive. But
his father _____ nervous when Chang is riding with
other teenagers. Chang's father _____ him money for
transportation. He reminds Chang to call him any time. Chang's father
_____ him, but he doesn't trust alcohol.

Write each sentence in the negative.

Negative

1. He knows his son's friends.   <u>*He doesn't know his son's friends.*</u>

2. I tell him to call me.   _____

3. We talk about drinking and
   driving.   _____
                                      _____

4. She rides with other teenagers.   _____

5. They trust their teenager.   _____

Listening

Listen to the dialog between Shen and Chang. Put a check next to what Shen says.

1. ____ a. I want you to drink alcohol.

   ____ b. I don't want you to drink alcohol.

2. ____ a. Teenagers don't make good decisions when they drink alcohol.

   ____ b. Teenagers don't make decisions when they drink alcohol.

3. ____ a. It is safe and it is legal.

   ____ b. It isn't safe and it isn't legal.

4. ____ a. But I feel nervous when you're riding with other parents.

   ____ b. But I feel nervous when you're riding with other teenagers.

5. ____ a. Never ride with a person who is drinking.

   ____ b. Never ride with a person who is driving.

6. ____ a. Here is some money for transportation.

   ____ b. Here is some money for trusting me.

7. ____ a. I can always pick up your friends. No questions. I promise.

   ____ b. I can always pick you up. No questions. I promise.

Pronunciation and Writing

Say the words. Write the number of syllables next to each word. Underline the stressed syllable in the two- and three-syllable words. The first one is done for you.

1. trust ___1___

2. promise ____

3. accidents ____

4. teenager ____

5. decisions ____

6. ride ____

7. parents ____

8. safe ____

9. money ____

10. drink ____

11. alcohol ____

12. nervous ____

Answer the questions.

Check the correct answer.

1. What does Shen talk about a lot?

   ____ a. his son

   ____ b. driving

   ____ c. alcohol

2. What does alcohol cause?

   ____ a. accidents

   ____ b. phone calls

   ____ c. transportation

3. How does Shen feel?

   ____ a. safe

   ____ b. nervous

   ____ c. bad

4. Why does Shen give Chang money?

   ____ a. for transportation

   ____ b. for alcohol

   ____ c. for his friends

LESSON 12: A Child with Pink Eye

Complete the story.

antibiotic	bacterial	itchy	pink
left	yellow	clean	several

Doctor Linzer is a pediatrician. Today he is examining Rachel's

_____ eye. It is red and _____. It has a
  1   2

thick _____ discharge. It looks like conjunctivitis, or
        3

_____ eye. She has a _____ infection in the
  4   5

eye. It spreads easily. Rachel's mother says _____ children
                                                6

at preschool have the same infection. Doctor Linzer writes a prescription

for _____ eye drops. He tells Rachel to keep her hands
      7

_____. She also can't touch her eyes with her hands.
  8

Write each sentence in the negative.

                                                    Negative

1. You need to take her home.   _You don't need to take her home._

2. It spreads easily.   _____

3. He writes a prescription   _____
   for eye drops.   _____

4. She washes her hands.   _____

5. I understand.   _____

Listening

Write the correct number next to each picture.

a. ____

c. ____

e. ____

b. ____

d. ____

What do they mean?

Listen to each sentence. Then circle what the person means.

1. a. It is before the usual time.   b. It is after the usual time.

2. a. It looks like red eye.   b. It looks like pink eye.

3. a. It spreads easily.   b. It doesn't spread easily.

4. a. She needs to get them for 24 hours.   b. She needs to get them for seven days.

5. a. She touches her eye.   b. She doesn't touch her eye.

Pronunciation and Writing

Complete each word from the story with two missing vowels: *a, e, i, o,* or *u.* Then practice saying the words.

1. app __ __ ntment

2. bacter __ __ l

3. spr __ __ ds

4. __ __ rly

5. prescript __ __ n

6. infect __ __ n

7. cl __ __ n

8. contagi __ __ s

9. __ __ sily

10. w __ __ k

11. r __ __ ches

12. ped __ __ trician

13. y __ __ rs

14. antib __ __ tic

15. presch __ __ l

Answer the questions.

Check the correct answer.

1. Why is Rachel's mother picking her up early?

____ a. She has a rash.

____ b. She has conjunctivitis.

____ c. She has an appointment.

2. Who does she make an appointment to see?

____ a. the preschool director

____ b. the pharmacist

____ c. the pediatrician

3. What is the prescription for?

____ a. antibiotic eye drops

____ b. glasses

____ c. pain medicine

4. Why is this infection a problem?

____ a. It's clean.

____ b. It's contagious.

____ c. It's pink.

LESSON 13: Translating at the Doctor's Office

Complete the sentences.

nods	hurts	talks
affects	tells	translates

1. Mi-Ok has arthritis. It _____ her hands.

2. It _____ to slice vegetables and hold utensils.

3. Her son _____ the doctor about his mother's problems.

4. The doctor _____ about arthritis medication.

5. Young-Jae _____ the information for his mother.

6. Mi-Ok _____ her head. She understands the information.

Write each sentence in the negative.

	Negative
1. It affects her hands.	*It doesn't affect her hands.*
2. She speaks Korean.	_____
3. I tell the doctor about her problems.	_____
4. He writes a prescription for her.	_____
5. You need your hands for cooking.	_____

Listening

Write the correct number next to each picture.

a. _____

c. _____

e. _____

b. _____

d. _____

What do they mean?

Listen to each sentence. Then circle what the person means.

1.a. Cooking is hard.
b. Cooking is easy.

2.a. He speaks Korean.
b. He speaks Korean and English.

3.a. Mi-Ok has other treatments.
b. Mi-Ok hears about other treatments.

4.a. She understands the information.
b. She doesn't understand the information.

5.a. Take the medicine.
b. Don't take the medicine.

Pronunciation and Writing

Say the words. Write the number of syllables next to each word. Underline the stressed syllable in the two- and three-syllable words. The first one is done for you.

1. arth<u>ri</u>tis   _3_   5. think   ____   9. injections ____

2. mother   ____   6. treatments   ____   10. pills   ____

3. slice   ____   7. prescriptions ____   11. translates ____

4. understands ____   8. affects   ____   12. pain   ____

Answer the questions.

Check the correct answer.

1. What does Mi-Ok have?

   ____ a. vegetables

   ____ b. arthritis

   ____ c. good luck

2. What is it difficult for her to do?

   ____ a. cook

   ____ b. speak Korean

   ____ c. go to restaurants

3. What does her son do at the doctor's office?

   ____ a. He picks up pots.

   ____ b. He translates.

   ____ c. He opens jars.

4. What is her prescription for?

   ____ a. injections

   ____ b. physical therapy

   ____ c. arthritis medication

LESSON 14: A Bad Cut

Complete the story.

minutes	knife	kitchen	towel
finger	manager	stitches	pressure

Helen is a _____ in a restaurant. She hears someone
say, "Ouch!" Helen runs into the _____. It is Javier.
"Are you okay?" asks Helen. Javier says he has a bad cut from a
sharp _____. He grabs a clean _____. He
wraps it tightly around his index _____. Helen wants to
see the cut, but Javier needs to apply _____. After 20
_____, Javier and Helen look at the cut. It's still bleeding a
lot. "You need _____," says Helen. "A doctor can help you."

Rewrite the sentence.

Rewrite the sentence with different subjects. Then write negative sentences.

Negative

1. He is using a very sharp knife.   <u>He isn't using a very sharp knife.</u>

2. I _____   _____

3. We _____   _____

4. She _____   _____

5. You _____   _____

Listening

Listen to the dialog between Javier and the doctor. Put a check next to what the doctor says.

1. ____ a. Try to keep your stitches dry for at least 12 hours.

 ____ b. Try to keep your stitches dry for at least 24 hours.

2. ____ a. You can wear the bandage for a few more days.

 ____ b. You can wear a bandage for a few more hours.

3. ____ a. Use the antibiotic ointment twice a day.

 ____ b. Use the antibiotic ointment once a day.

4. ____ a. I want to see you again in four days.

 ____ b. I want to see you again in five days.

5. ____ a. But come in immediately if you see any sign of infection.

 ____ b. But call me immediately if you see any sign of infection.

6. ____ a. Look for redness, drainage, warmth, or swelling.

 ____ b. Look for redness, changes, warmth, or sweating.

7. ____ a. Don't worry. I have instructions for you on this paper.

 ____ b. Don't worry. I have instructions for you on this prescription.

Pronunciation and Writing

Complete each word from the story with two missing vowels: *a, e, i, o,* or *u.* Then practice saying the words.

1. t __ w __ l

2. kn __ f __

3. __ n __ on

4. bl __ ed __ ng

5. cl __ n __ c

6. f __ ng __ r

7. em __ rg __ ncy

8. st __ tch __ s

9. tet __ n __ s

10. r __ sta __ rant

11. c __ tt __ ng

12. __ ro __ nd

13. pr __ ss __ re

14. s __ st __ r

15. __ nd __ x

Answer the questions.

Check the correct answer.

1. What slips and cuts Javier's finger?

____ a. a large onion

____ b. a sharp knife

____ c. a clean towel

2. What does Javier need to do?

____ a. apply pressure

____ b. put on ointment

____ c. finish cutting

3. How is the cut after 20 minutes?

____ a. long and deep

____ b. much better

____ c. still bleeding a lot

4. What does Javier get at the clinic?

____ a. onion soup

____ b. stitches and a tetanus shot

____ c. a day off

Listening Exercise Prompts

Lesson 1

Write the correct number next to each picture. (p. 5)

1. Zahra is looking for orange juice.
2. Lela points to a big orange bottle.
3. Zahra looks at the Nutrition Facts label.
4. Zahra puts down the bottle.

Write the percentages you hear. (p. 5)

1. 80%
2. 40%
3. 10%
4. 60%
5. 20%
6. 100%
7. 30%
8. 50%
9. 90%
10. 70%

Lesson 2

Listening (p. 8)

I'd like to order the grilled halibut.

Very well.

You need to know that I am allergic to shellfish.

Okay.

I have a message for the cook.

Sure. What is it?

Please tell him to be careful with my dinner.

What should he do?

My food cannot touch shellfish.

Anything else?

Ask him to clean the counter, grill, and utensils very well.

I'll tell him.

Thanks. I can get very sick from eating a tiny amount.

Lesson 3

Write the correct number next to each picture. (p. 11)

1. Salman works long hours.
2. He worries about sending his children to college.
3. Sometimes Salman feels pain.
4. He needs to relax more.

Write the dollar amounts you hear. (p. 11)

1. That's $45, please.
2. Your total is $90.
3. That comes to $65.
4. It costs $70.
5. The ticket costs $25.
6. You need to pay $60.
7. It's $15.
8. It comes to $50.
9. This bill is for $85.
10. They cost $30.

Lesson 4

Write the correct number next to each picture. (p. 14)

1. Squat down. Bend at your hips and knees only.
2. Lift the box slowly.
3. Hold the box close to your body.
4. Take small steps.
5. Put the box down. Squat with hips and knees again.

What do they mean? (p. 14)

1. Ugh. I can't lift it.
2. No! You can hurt your back!
3. Can you give me a hand?
4. I appreciate you telling me that.
5. Let's lift it together.

Lesson 5

Listening (p. 17)

How is your shoulder feeling?

Much better. I like the exercise.

It looks good. You can stop going to physical therapy now.

Really?

Just continue your exercises at home.

Okay. What about housework?

It's fine. You can sweep and vacuum again.

Never mind. My husband can do that.

But be careful on the steps. You don't want another surgery.

I sure don't.

Do you have any other questions?

Yes. When can I start swimming?

You can start right away. Swimming is great exercise.

Lesson 6

Write the correct number next to each picture. (p. 20)

1. Eric has a healthy diet.
2. He brushes his teeth twice a day.
3. He visits the dentist regularly.
4. He takes 18 inches of dental floss.
5. He gently cleans between his teeth and gums.

What do they mean? (p. 20)

1. Do you floss?
2. I avoid sugary sodas.
3. A toothbrush can't clean all areas.
4. You want to keep your beautiful smile.
5. See you in six months.

Lesson 7

Write the correct number next to each picture. (p. 23)

1. Alina washes her hands with warm, soapy water.
2. She cuts the chicken into small pieces.
3. She almost puts the vegetables down on the same cutting board.
4. Svetlana hands Alina a different cutting board.
5. Svetlana washes the plastic cutting board with hot, soapy water.

What do they mean? (p. 23)

1. Wash your hands well.
2. The chicken can have bacteria.
3. We keep raw meat away from other food.
4. Put one teaspoon of chlorine bleach in one quart of water.
5. Put the towel in the laundry.

Lesson 8

Circle the telephone number you hear. (p. 26)

1. 555-1489
2. 555-0926
3. 555-8317
4. 555-2058
5. 555-3180

Write the number of refills you hear (p. 26)

1. You have two more refills.
2. She has four more refills.
3. I have no more refills.
4. He has one more refill.
5. They have three more refills.
6. I have five more refills.

Lesson 9

Listening (p. 29)

Poison Control. May I help you?

My son just ate a lot of vitamins!

Does he have any symptoms?

No, but he only ate them about five minutes ago.

How old is he?

He's four years old.

How much does he weigh?

He weighs 42 pounds.

What kind of vitamins?

The Dancing Dog Vitamins.

How many did he take?

I'm not sure. I think about 20.

And who are you and what is your relationship to the child?

I am Kate Browning, his mother.

Lesson 10

Write the correct number next to each picture. (p. 32)

1. Greta is packing a suitcase for her father.
2. She puts his health insurance information inside her purse.
3. Greta gets all his prescription drugs in their original containers.
4. She gives the allergy list to his doctor.

5. The nurse records everything on his chart.

What do they mean? (p. 32)

1. He needs to be in the hospital for a few days.
2. The drugs are in their original containers.
3. He is allergic to two antibiotics.
4. You're all set, Dad.
5. I want something to read.

Lesson 11

Listening (p. 35)

I don't want you to drink alcohol.

I don't drink, Dad.

Teenagers don't make good decisions when they drink alcohol.

I know.

It isn't safe and it isn't legal.

You can trust me.

But I feel nervous when you're riding with other teenagers.

My friends are okay, Dad.

Never ride with a person who is drinking.

I won't.

Here is some money for transportation.

Thanks.

I can always pick you up. No questions. I promise.

Lesson 12

Write the correct number next to each picture. (p. 38)

1. Rachel is in the preschool office.
2. She is rubbing her eye a lot.
3. Rachel's mother makes an appointment to see the pediatrician.
4. Rachel needs to use antibiotic eye drops for one week.
5. She needs to keep her hands clean.

What do they mean? (p. 38)

1. Her mother is picking her up early.
2. It looks like conjunctivitis.
3. This infection is very contagious.

4. Rachel needs to take eye drops for one week.
5. Rachel rubs her eye.

Lesson 13

Write the correct number next to each picture. (p. 41)

1. It hurts to slice vegetables.
2. She can't open jars.
3. The doctor talks about arthritis medication.
4. Young-Jae translates the information for his mother.
5. Mi-Ok wants to eat out tonight.

What do they mean? (p. 41)

1. It is difficult for her to cook.
2. Young-Jae helps his mother and the doctor understand each other.
3. The doctor talks about injections, physical therapy, and surgery.
4. Mi-Ok nods her head.
5. Let's try the medication.

Lesson 14

Listening (p. 44)

Try to keep your stitches dry for at least 24 hours.

Do you want me to keep my stitches covered?

You can wear the bandage for a few more days.

How often do I put on the ointment?

Use the antibiotic ointment twice a day.

When do you want me to come back?

I want to see you again in five days.

I can do that.

But come in immediately if you see any sign of infection.

What are the signs of an infection?

Look for redness, drainage, warmth, or swelling.

I hope I can remember all of this.

Don't worry. I have instructions for you on this paper.